RICHARD PRESCOTT

The Bonetti
Inheritance

HEINEMANN ELT

HEINEMANN GUIDED READERS

INTERMEDIATE LEVEL

Series Editor: John Milne

PRE

The Heinemann Guided Readers provide a choice of enjoyable reading material for learners of English. The series is published at five levels – Starter, Beginner, Elementary, Intermediate and Upper. At **Intermediate Level**, the control of content and language has the following main features:

Information Control

Information which is vital to the understanding of the story is presented in an easily assimilated manner and is repeated when necessary. Difficult allusion and metaphor are avoided and cultural backgrounds are made explicit.

Structure Control

Most of the structures used in the Readers will be familiar to students who have completed an elementary course of English. Other grammatical features may occur, but their use is made clear through context and reinforcement. This ensures that the reading, as well as being enjoyable, provides a continual learning situation for the students. Sentences are limited in most cases to a maximum of three clauses and within sentences there is a balanced use of simple adverbial and adjectival phrases. Great care is taken with pronoun reference.

Vocabulary Control

There is a basic vocabulary of approximately 1,600 words. Help is given to the students in the form of illustrations which are closely related to the text.

Glossary

Some difficult words and phrases in this book are important for understanding the story. Some of these words are explained in the story, some are shown in the pictures, and others are marked with a number like this ...[3] Words with a number are explained in the Glossary on page 61.

Contents

1

A Special Business Agreement

It was three o'clock in the afternoon and the restaurant was almost empty. The last customers were finishing their meals. The waiters were quietly clearing the plates and glasses from the tables. Mario Bonetti, the owner of the restaurant, was sitting outside in the sunshine and drinking coffee.

The restaurant was in a little square. The square had a fountain in the middle. Mario listened to the sound of the fountain. It was a pleasant, gentle sound. The town was quiet now. The shopkeepers were resting after lunch. They would open again at half past three. Mario sat drinking his coffee and thinking. He was thinking, as usual, about money.

Mario was a successful businessman. He owned the best and most expensive restaurant in town. He was successful, but he was greedy. Mario was always trying to find ways of making more money.

A large white Mercedes drove into the square and stopped outside the restaurant. A man in his forties[1] got out. He was tall and handsome and he was wearing an expensive suit. His name was Luca Pagani. Pagani was well-known in the town because he was a member of the Town Council. As a councillor, he knew lots of important people. If you were in business, Pagani was a useful man to know[2].

Mario looked up. He was pleased to see Pagani.

'You're late for lunch,' Mario said. 'The chef will be going home soon. But I'm sure we can get something for you.'

'Don't worry,' said Pagani. 'I haven't come for lunch. Is there a place where we can talk?'

'Sit down,' said Mario, pointing to the chair opposite him.

'Not here,' said Pagani. 'I want to talk to you in private.'

'Oh,' said Mario. 'Come with me.'

They went into a small room at the back of the restaurant. It was Mario's office. Mario closed the door and the two men sat down.

'What can I do for you?' asked Mario.

'First of all, you must promise me something,' said Pagani.

'And what's that?' asked Mario.

'You must keep this conversation a secret.'

'Of course. What do you want to talk about?'

'About business.'

Mario looked at Pagani for a moment. He was interested.

'I'd like to make an agreement with you,' Pagani said. 'A special business agreement. You could make a lot of money.'

Mario's eyes shone with greed.

'Are you interested?' asked Pagani calmly.

'Oh yes, certainly,' Mario said.

'I said the agreement was a special one,' said Pagani. 'You understand what that means, don't you?'

Mario knew what Pagani meant. But he said, 'Please explain.'

'It's an agreement that must be kept secret. You must tell no one about it, or there'll be trouble.'

'With the police?' asked Mario.

'Perhaps,' said Pagani. 'Are you still interested? There won't be much danger for you. And you can make a lot of money.'

'How much?' asked Mario.

'A fortune. You could buy ten restaurants like this.'

Mario smiled. 'And there isn't much danger, you say.'

'Very little danger,' said Pagani. 'All we have to do is keep quiet and be careful.'

'Then I'm interested,' said Mario. 'You have my promise. I'll keep quiet. Now, tell me, what is this special business agreement?'

'It's simple,' said Pagani. 'But first let me show you a few things. Come with me and I'll explain.'

2

A Piece of Land

Pagani drove out of the town. They passed some factories on a main road and Pagani stopped the Mercedes. On their left, there were a few houses. On the other side of the road, there was flat, open ground. There were no fences around the ground and it looked deserted[3].

'Do you know who owns this land?' asked Pagani.

'No,' said Mario. 'Isn't it council property?'

Pagani shook his head. 'Oh, no. This land belongs to a big international computer company.'

'I see,' said Mario. And then he added, 'Or rather, I don't see. What's this got to do with our special business agreement?'

'This computer company is going to build its main office here. There'll be tall office blocks[4] on this land. And there's also going to be a new research centre[5].'

'Oh,' said Mario. He did not understand why Pagani was telling him this.

'More than two thousand people will work here,' Pagani continued. 'About eighteen thousand people are now living in this town. Another two thousand families will come to live here. Think what a difference that will make.'

'It'll mean more work for everyone.'

'Exactly,' said Pagani. 'The town will need new shops, schools, houses . . . And the price of houses and land will go up.'

'Of course,' agreed Mario.

'The price of land,' continued Pagani, 'will soon be twice as much as it is now.'

'The more land you own the better!' said Mario, smiling.

'And if you buy land at the present price, you'll make a lot of money later – a very big profit.'

'This computer company is going to build its main office here,' said Pagani.

'Is this the special agreement?'

'Yes,' said Pagani. 'We can buy land now and build houses and shops. Then, at the right time, we'll sell everything.'

'But everyone else will try to do the same,' said Mario.

'Yes,' said Pagani. 'But we have an advantage[6]. *We* know that the computer company plans to build its main office and research centre here. No one else does. And it will remain a secret for some months.'

'How do you know?' asked Mario.

Pagani looked at Mario. 'Friends, Mr Bonetti. I have a lot of very useful friends.'

Pagani started the car and said, 'There's something else I want to show you. I think you'll find it interesting.'

Pagani drove on a short distance and then turned down a quiet country road. Pagani stopped the car. There were fields on both sides of the road. In the distance, there was an old farmhouse.

'And this,' said Pagani proudly, 'is where we're going to build our shops and houses.'

Mario was surprised. He did not know what to say.

'Well,' said Pagani, 'what do you think? It's a good piece of land, isn't it?'

'But this is my brother's farm! You can't build here.'

'But I've heard that your brother is very ill and will soon be dead.'

Mario looked down sadly. 'That's true,' he said. 'The doctors say he may die in a few days.'

'Very good,' said Pagani happily. 'That's better than I thought.'

'What?' said Mario, shocked.

'I'm a hard man, Mr Bonetti,' Pagani said. 'And I like to speak plainly. When your brother dies, we'll be able to get the land.'

'Wait a minute,' said Mario. 'My brother has a son. I won't inherit the land. The land won't belong to me. The farm will belong to my nephew.'

'Yes,' said Pagani, 'but you can buy the farm from your nephew. Then we'll get a builder to build the shops and houses. And when the computer company arrives, we'll make a fortune.'

Mario was silent for a moment. Then he said, 'But you're forgetting something. This is farmland. It isn't building land. It's against the law to build houses and offices on farmland. You can only use the land for agriculture.'

Pagani smiled. 'That's why you must buy it. Farmland is much cheaper than building land.'

'Yes, but how can we build on it afterwards?' said Mario. 'It'll be against the law.'

'The law can be changed,' said Pagani. 'Don't worry about that.'

'I don't understand.'

'The town always needs new building land,' Pagani explained. 'And the Town Planning Department[7] often has to find new land for building. As a member of the Town Council, one of my jobs is to suggest to the Town Planning Department which land can be, built on. I can suggest making new building land here.'

'I see,' said Mario quietly. 'But what about my nephew?'

'What about him?' asked Pagani, surprised.

'Well,' said Mario. 'I won't be able to tell him the truth, will I?'

Pagani laughed loudly. 'That happens all the time in business,' he said.

'Yes,' said Mario. 'But he is my nephew.'

'You'll pay him well for his land,' said Pagani. 'If the land increases in value, it isn't your fault.'

'Tell me something. Is all this legal?'

Pagani laughed again. 'It's legal to buy and sell land,' he said.

'But this is not simply buying and selling land,' replied Mario. 'We'll have to tell lies.'

'Oh, that isn't important.'

'But you're a town councillor,' said Mario. 'If anyone finds out about this you may go to prison.'

'I have the most dangerous part to play in this business,' Pagani said. 'I understand that. But everything will be all right if we keep our agreement secret. Nothing must be written down. That's why we have to trust each other. Is that clear?'

Mario nodded his head. 'It's clear,' he said. 'You can trust me, Mr Pagani.'

3

Roberto Makes a Promise

Mario's nephew, Roberto, was twenty-two. He was a hard working young man. Life for Roberto was difficult. His mother had died some years ago, and now his father was dying too.

Roberto had worked all day on the farm and he was tired and hungry. He ate supper in the farmhouse kitchen, then he went to his father's room. His father was lying in bed and seemed to be sleeping. Roberto sat down near the bed. Slowly his father's eyes opened.

'How are you today?' Roberto asked.

'Not too bad,' said his father.

This was not true. He felt terrible. There were pains all over his body. He was tired and weak.

'Have you slept?' Roberto asked.

'Not much,' said his father. 'But I've been thinking a lot.'

'What about?'

'Many things,' his father answered slowly. 'But mostly about you. I'm very worried, Roberto.'

'You mustn't worry about me.'

'Soon you'll be on your own.'

'Don't say that,' said Roberto.

'It's true, Roberto,' his father said. 'We both know that I'm dying.'

Roberto was silent.

'Life won't be easy for you,' his father said.

'I'll be all right,' replied Roberto.

'The farm will be yours, of course,' his father said. 'But there'll be a lot of work for one man to do.'

'I know.'

Roberto felt very sad. He looked at his father's thin, pale face. His father was only fifty-four years old. He had always been strong and healthy. This terrible illness had come so suddenly.

'You do like farming, don't you, Roberto?' his father asked.

'Yes, of course,' replied Roberto. 'Why do you ask?'

'Our family has always worked on the land here. I hope you'll go on working and living here.'

'Why shouldn't I stay here?'

'It's a hard life working on a farm. If you sold the farm, you could have a different life.'

'I don't want a different life,' said Roberto.

'I'm happy about that,' his father said. 'I don't want you to sell our family's land.'

'I won't sell it. I promise you.'

'The world is changing. Young men want a better life than their fathers had. But I hope that you'll keep the farm. And, of course, I hope that you'll be happy here.'

'Rest now,' Roberto said. 'You mustn't worry about me or the farm.'

Roberto's father closed his eyes. A few minutes later he was sleeping. Roberto stood silently by the bed. He looked down at his dying father. Roberto stood there for a long time in the

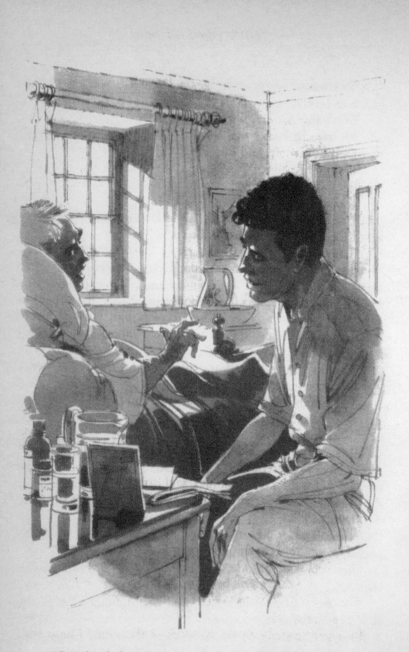

'Our family has always worked on the land here. I hope
you'll go on working and living here.'

dark room. It was very late when he finally went downstairs again.

4

Mario Offers to Help

Three days later Roberto's father died. Now both of Roberto's parents were dead and he felt very lonely. Many people came to see Roberto. But there was only one person that Roberto really wanted to see. This was Valeria, his girlfriend.

Valeria Conti lived in the same town. She and Roberto had known each other for a long time. Valeria liked riding horses. She had a beautiful black horse which she kept on Roberto's farm. She went to the farm every day to look after her horse and to ride it.

Valeria was a university student. She was studying architecture. She had almost finished her course and now she was trying to find a job.

After the funeral, a few friends and relatives came back to the farmhouse. They ate a simple meal together and talked quietly. When Roberto was alone in the kitchen, his uncle, Mario, came to speak to him.

'Please let me know if you need help,' Mario said.

'Thanks,' said Roberto.

'Will you be all right on your own here?'

'Yes, I'll be fine.'

'Have you thought about the future?'

'What do you mean?'

'One person can't do all the work on the farm,' Mario said.

'You'll need help. You'll have to employ workers.'

'You're probably right,' said Roberto. He had not thought about these problems. And he did not really want to think about them.

'But it won't be easy for you to find farm workers,' Mario went on. 'People don't want to work on the land. Farm workers don't earn enough money.'

'I don't want to worry about these problems now,' said Roberto sadly.

'Of course,' said Mario. 'But you'll have to think about these things soon. That's reality.'

'I know,' said Roberto.

'Perhaps I'll be able to help you,' said Mario. 'When you're feeling better, we can have a talk together.'

'I don't know how you can help,' said Roberto. 'But thanks anyway.'

'Well,' said Mario slowly, 'if you want to sell the farm . . .'

'Oh, I don't want to sell the farm.'

'Not now perhaps. But you may change your mind in the future.'

'I don't think so,' said Roberto.

'If you sell,' said Mario, 'you won't have to worry about anything. And you'll be rich. Just think about it.'

'I told you,' said Roberto. 'I won't sell it.'

'All right,' said Mario. 'But if you change your mind, come and speak to me.'

Valeria came into the kitchen.

'Here you are!' Valeria said to Roberto. 'I thought you were hiding from me!'

'I've been talking to Uncle Mario,' Roberto said.

'Well, I'll leave you two alone,' said Mario. 'Don't forget what I've told you, Roberto. If you need any help, come and tell me.'

'Thank you, Uncle Mario,' Roberto said.

5

Something to Celebrate

Mario was right. There was too much work to do on the farm. Roberto and his father had done the work together before. Roberto had done all the work on his own while his father was ill. Now Roberto was alone and he knew it was too difficult for him to continue doing everything.

There were twenty-five cows on the farm. They had to be milked twice a day, and the cowsheds had to be cleaned. Then there were the chickens – a shed full of them. And, of course, there was other work to do in the fields. Valeria helped Roberto as much as she could. But Valeria was busy with her studies. She had one more university examination to do. After that, she would have her degree in architecture.

A month after Roberto's father had died, Roberto was working in the kitchen. It was after seven o'clock in the evening.

Valeria had not been to the farm all day. She had been busy at the university. Roberto was expecting her to come in at any moment. He knew she would have some important news.

She arrived at half past seven. She opened the door and came into the kitchen.

'Well?' Roberto said.

Valeria did not say anything.

'How was it?' asked Roberto. 'Aren't you going to tell me?'

A big smile came on Valeria's face. Roberto knew the news was good.

'I've passed my last university exam,' Valeria said. 'What do you think of that?'

Roberto kissed her. 'Wonderful!' he shouted.

Roberto opened the fridge and took out a bottle of champagne. 'We've got something to celebrate,' he said.

'I can't believe it,' said Valeria, sitting down. 'Now I've finished everything. I don't have to take any more exams.'

'And now you're an architect, you'll have to get a job!' said Roberto.

Valeria smiled and took an envelope from her bag. 'Read this,' she said.

She handed the envelope to Roberto. He took out the letter that was inside and began to read:

> *Architects' Office*
> *Town Planning Department*
> *20th June*

Dear Ms Conti

Thank you for coming for an interview on 10th June. We are pleased to offer you the post of Assistant Architect in the Architects' Office. The starting date for the job is Monday, 3rd August.

We look forward to hearing from you.
> *Yours sincerely*

> *Giorgio Galli*
> *Chief Architect*

'Valeria!' said Roberto. 'You didn't tell me you had applied for this job.'

'I wanted to surprise you,' Valeria said.

'You've certainly surprised me. This is great news. I'm very, very pleased.'

Roberto put two glasses on the table and filled them with champagne.

'Congratulations!' he said, holding up his glass.

'Thank you,' said Valeria.

They touched glasses and drank some champagne. Suddenly there was a loud knock at the door. Roberto went to open the door.

'Uncle Mario!' he said. 'Come in.'

Mario came into the kitchen. 'Are you all right?' Mario asked. 'I'm sorry I haven't come to see you before, but I've been very busy.'

Mario noticed the bottle of champagne and the glasses.

'We're celebrating,' Valeria said. 'Would you like a glass?'

'Thanks,' said Mario, and he sat down at the table. 'What are you celebrating?' he asked.

Roberto took a glass from the cupboard and filled it with champagne. He gave the glass to Mario.

'It's been a lucky day for me,' said Valeria. 'I've passed my last university exam. And I've also had an offer of a job.'

'Congratulations!' Mario said, and he took a drink from his glass.

'Thank you,' said Valeria.

'And what kind of job is it?' asked Mario.

'Assistant Architect in the Town Planning Department – in the Architects' Office,' said Valeria.

'Is the job in this town?' Mario asked.

'Yes,' said Valeria. 'I'm lucky, aren't I? I start work at the beginning of August.'

'That's wonderful,' said Mario. 'And what about your young man?' he added, turning to Roberto. 'How are you getting on?'

'I'm fine,' Roberto said. 'I've been very busy here on the farm. There's a lot of work to do.'

'I'm sure it's difficult for you,' Mario said.

'Yes, but I like hard work.'

'Are you going to keep the farm?' Mario asked.

'Of course,' said Roberto.

Mario refilled his glass of champagne and took a drink. 'I'll be honest with you, Roberto,' he said slowly. 'I'd like to buy your farm. If you agree . . .'

'But I don't agree, Uncle,' said Roberto firmly[8]. 'I don't want to sell the farm.'

'Roberto, you must listen to me,' said Mario. 'I can pay you a lot of money. You'll be rich. Think about that.'

'I've told you, Uncle,' said Roberto. 'I won't sell the farm. I can't sell it.'

'Can't?' asked Mario.

'I don't want to sell it,' said Roberto. He was angry now. 'I like working on the farm. It's my life. And I promised my father that I would stay here.'

Valeria looked at Mario and said, 'May I ask you something?'

'Of course,' replied Mario.

'You aren't a farmer,' Valeria said. 'Why do you want to buy the farm?'

Mario smiled. 'The farmhouse is a lovely old house. I'd restore[9] it and come and live here. And then I'd like to keep horses. I'd have some stables here. People would come and learn to ride. I'd like that.'

'Well, I'm sorry, Uncle,' Roberto said. 'You can forget the idea. I'm not going to sell the farm. There's nothing more to say.'

'All right,' said Mario. He stood up and walked to the door. 'Goodbye,' he said. 'But think about what I've said, Roberto.'

'Goodbye, Uncle,' said Roberto. 'There's nothing to think about.'

Mario went out and closed the door behind him. For a moment, Valeria and Roberto sat silently at the table. Then they washed the wine glasses and prepared to go out for dinner. They had a lot to celebrate.

'Roberto, you must listen to me,' said Mario. 'I can pay you a lot of money. You'll be rich.'

6

A Few Problems

Mario went immediately to his restaurant. He had arranged to meet Pagani there at eight o'clock. The waiters had prepared a table in a room at the back of the restaurant. Mario and Pagani were going to eat dinner and talk about their special business agreement.

Mario was unhappy and silent. The special business agreement was giving him more problems than he had expected. He sat down and drank some wine while he waited for Pagani to arrive.

Pagani was late. He was always late for appointments. Pagani liked to make people wait for him.

At last Pagani came into the restaurant. He gave his coat to a waiter and sat down opposite Mario.

'I think you've got some bad news for me,' said Pagani calmly.

Mario moved about in his chair. 'There . . . there are a few problems,' Mario said. 'How did you know?'

'I knew as soon as I saw your face,' Pagani said.

'It's my nephew . . .' began Mario.

'I suppose he doesn't want to sell the farm,' said Pagani.

'He'll never sell it, Mr Pagani,' Mario said. 'I'm sure of that.'

There was a bottle of wine on the table and Pagani poured himself a glass.

'All right,' Pagani said. 'We'll have to make him change his mind.'

'My nephew likes farming,' Mario explained. 'That's the real problem. And, also, he promised his father that he wouldn't sell the farm.'

Pagani laughed. 'That's not a problem,' he said. 'A promise can be broken[10].'

'Unfortunately my nephew is an honest young man,' said

Mario. 'I don't think he'll break his promise.'

'What about money?' asked Pagani. 'How much did you offer to pay?'

'I didn't say how much I would pay. I told him that he'd be rich. But he's not interested in money.'

'Everyone's interested in money,' Pagani said. 'Speak to him again. Tell him he'll have so much money that he won't need to work again.'

'There's another thing that you should know,' said Mario. 'My nephew has a girlfriend, Valeria Conti.'

'Well?' said Pagani.

'She's an architect,' said Mario. 'And she's going to work in the Town Planning Department, in the Architects' Office. She might give us problems.'

Pagani thought for a moment. 'You're right,' he said. 'In the Architects' Office she would know about new building developments[11]. She might find out if your nephew's land becomes building land. We must stop her getting the job. We don't want her in the Architects' Office.'

'I'm afraid we can't do that,' said Mario. 'She starts work at the beginning of August.'

Pagani was not worried. He picked up a piece of bread and started to eat it.

'I can arrange something, Mr Bonetti,' Pagani said. 'Don't worry.'

Mario looked at Pagani and thought, Pagani is a wonderful man. He can do anything and solve any problem.

'About your nephew . . .' Pagani said, '. . . I'd like to see him. Perhaps I can make him change his mind. Why don't you invite him and his girlfriend to come here to your restaurant next Saturday night?'

'All right,' Mario said.

'I'll come about nine o'clock, after they've eaten. You can introduce me. But your nephew mustn't know that the meeting has been arranged. Do you understand?'

'Perfectly,' said Mario.

'Good,' said Pagani.

The waiter came with their meal. Pagani poured out some more wine for himself and for Mario.

'Cheers!' Pagani said. He took a drink from his glass. 'Everything will be all right, you'll see.'

7

Pagani is Busy

Pagani was in his office in the Town Hall very early next morning.

'Ask the Chief Architect to come and see me,' he told his secretary.

Soon after nine o'clock, Giorgio Galli, the Chief Architect, arrived in Pagani's office.

'What's the problem?' asked Galli, sitting down.

'It's about money,' Pagani said. 'The Department of Town Planning has spent too much money this year. I'm asking all the offices in the department to spend less money. We'll have to save money.'

'What do you want me to do?' asked Galli. 'The Architects' Office is very small. We can't save much money.'

'You're planning to have a new Assistant Architect, I believe,' said Pagani.

'That's right,' replied Galli.

'Well, I'm sorry,' said Pagani, 'but you can't have a new Assistant Architect at the moment.'

'It's too late to change our plan now,' said Galli. 'The new person will start at the beginning of August.'

'I'm sorry about that,' said Pagani, 'but you'll have to tell this person that there isn't a job in the Architects' Office now.'

'I can't do that, Mr Pagani,' Galli said firmly.

Pagani looked straight at Galli. 'Mr Galli, I've explained the situation to you,' he said. 'Please do what I ask. You can have your new Assistant Architect in a few months' time. At the moment, we must all spend less money.'

'Why didn't you tell me this earlier?' asked Galli. 'You knew that I was looking for a new Assistant Architect.'

'I'm sorry,' said Pagani slowly. 'I don't want this to happen, but I have no choice. We must save money.'

Galli was angry when he left Pagani's office. He wondered what Pagani had said to the other people in the Planning Department. Galli decided to find out. He wanted to know how much money the other offices were saving. But first he had an unpleasant job to do. He had to write to Valeria Conti, telling her the bad news.

———

Pagani was busy most of the day. There were a lot of people that he wanted to see. In the afternoon, he drove to a dirty old factory near the edge of town. There was a high wall all round the factory. Metal gates opened into a small courtyard. On the left, there was an old stone building. This was the factory. On the right, there were a few offices. Pagani went inside one of the offices.

'Mr Goldoni is expecting[12] me,' Pagani said to the secretary as he walked past.

Pagani knocked on the door and walked into Goldoni's office without waiting for an answer. Goldoni was sitting at his desk, writing. There were papers everywhere. Goldoni looked up. He hated Pagani.

'Oh, it's you,' Goldoni said.

'Yes,' said Pagani. 'And you know what I've come for, don't you?'

Goldoni stood up and walked over to a metal safe[13] in the corner of the room. He opened the safe and took out a large envelope. He gave the envelope to Pagani.

'How much is here?' asked Pagani.

'Five hundred thousand lire,' said Goldoni. 'That's what I always give you.'

'Next month you'll have to give me eight hundred thousand lire,' Pagani said calmly.

'But that's too much, Mr Pagani,' Goldoni said. 'I can't pay you that much.'

'You can pay it,' said Pagani. 'If you don't pay, I'll close your factory. Do you understand?'

Goldoni was silent.

'Goodbye, Mr Goldoni,' Pagani said. 'See you next month.'

Pagani walked out and shut the door behind him.

8

Bad News

About a week later, on Thursday morning, Roberto was working in the farmyard. Just before lunch, Valeria arrived. Roberto was surprised. He had not expected her until the evening.

Roberto saw immediately that she had been crying.

'What's the matter?' he asked. Valeria began to cry again.

'Come on. Let's go inside,' said Roberto. 'Then you can tell me what's happened.'

Roberto led her into the kitchen and they sat down at the

Goldoni opened the safe and took out a large envelope. He gave the envelope to Pagani.

table. Valeria dried her eyes and took a letter from her bag

'I got this letter from the Town Planning Department this morning,' she said. 'They can't give me the job.'

'What?' said Roberto, surprised.

She gave the letter to Roberto and he read it:

Architects' Office
Town Planning Department
26th June

Dear Ms Conti

I wrote to you on 20th June offering you the job of Assistant Architect. Since then, there have been some unexpected changes in the Planning Department.

For this reason, no new Assistant Architect can be appointed in our office at the moment. Sadly, therefore, I am now unable to offer you the job.

Yours sincerely

Giorgio Galli
Chief Architect

Roberto folded the letter and gave it back to Valeria.

'I'm very sorry, Valeria,' he said. 'This is terrible news.'

'It's not right,' Valeria said angrily. 'Last week they told me that I had the job. And now this letter tells me I can't have it. Why did they change their minds?'

'You're right to be angry,' said Roberto.

'Well, I'm going to see Mr Galli,' Valeria said. 'I want him to explain. He can't change his mind without a good reason.'

———

Immediately after lunch, Valeria went to see Mr Galli in the Town Hall. As soon as Valeria walked into his office, Galli knew why she had come.

'You want to talk to me about the letter, don't you?' he said.

Valeria nodded her head.

'Let's go out and have a cup of coffee,' Galli said. 'Then we'll be able to talk in private.'

'All right,' said Valeria.

They walked to a quiet bar near the Town Hall. There was an empty table in a corner. They sat down and Mr Galli ordered coffee.

'I'm very sorry about what has happened,' Galli said.

'I'm sorry too,' Valeria replied. 'Why did you change your mind about giving me the job?'

'The truth is,' began Galli, 'I didn't change my mind. I wanted to give you the job, but someone stopped me.'

'What do you mean?' asked Valeria.

Galli was silent for a moment. He was thinking about how much he should tell her.

'It's possible that someone deliberately[14] stopped me giving you the job,' he said finally. 'I can't explain the facts in any other way. Someone didn't want you to have the job of Assistant Architect.'

'But why?' asked Valeria.

'I don't know,' Galli said. 'Can you think of anyone who doesn't want you to have the job?'

'No, I can't think of anyone,' said Valeria.

'Are you sure?'

'Completely sure.'

'Do you know a man named Pagani?' asked Galli.

'No,' said Valeria. 'Who is he?'

'Pagani is the councillor in charge of the Town Planning Department,' Galli said. 'He's the person who stopped me giving you the job.'

'But I don't know this man Pagani,' Valeria said. 'Why doesn't he want me to work in the Architects' Office?'

'I'm not sure,' said Galli.

The waiter came with their coffee. Galli became silent again. He looked down at his coffee cup.

'But I don't know this man Pagani,' Valeria said. 'Why doesn't he
want me to work in the Architects' Office?'

'Perhaps I've said too much,' he said at last. 'Perhaps I'm imagining[15] all this. I'm sorry, Miss Conti. Please forget what I've said.'

———

Valeria could not forget what Galli had told her. Galli had looked very unhappy. He had been afraid to say too much. Valeria wondered what Galli knew about Pagani. It was clear to Valeria that Galli had not told her everything. Valeria thought about these things as she went home. She had wanted Galli to explain to her why she could not have the job. But Galli had not explained anything. He had made Valeria more confused[16].

9

Pagani Has a Plan

The next day Mario invited Valeria and Roberto to have dinner in his restaurant. On Saturday evening, Roberto and Valeria went to the restaurant. It was full of people.

'I've got a table prepared for you,' Mario said when Valeria and Roberto arrived.

In the middle of the table, there was a vase of flowers. They were red roses. A little card said: *For Valeria, with best wishes*.

'Thank you very much,' Valeria said. 'The flowers are beautiful.'

'Beautiful flowers for a beautiful young lady,' Mario said, smiling.

Valeria laughed.

'Now you two must enjoy yourselves this evening,' Mario went on. 'I'll give you the best meal you've ever had.'

Mario kept his promise. It was indeed a wonderful meal.

While Valeria and Roberto were eating their dessert[17], Mario sat down at the table with them. The three of them talked together.

After a few minutes, Mario asked Roberto about the farm.

'How are you getting on, Roberto?' he asked. 'Are you enjoying all the hard work?'

'Oh, yes,' Roberto said.

'I can't believe it,' Mario said. 'You have so little free time. You never have holidays. What do you say, Valeria? Wouldn't you like to see Roberto more often?'

'Of course,' said Valeria. 'But I want Roberto to be happy, and anyway, I like helping on the farm too. I keep my horse there.'

'Oh, yes,' Mario said, 'I'd forgotten about that.'

Mario was about to say something else when he saw someone come into the restaurant. He was a tall man with dark hair. Mario waved at him. The tall man walked through the restaurant to where Mario, Valeria and Roberto were sitting.

'Luca, this is my nephew, Roberto, and his girlfriend, Valeria Conti,' Mario said to the man.

'Pleased to meet you, Mr . . .?' said Roberto.

'Pagani,' the man said. 'Luca Pagani.'

Pagani shook hands with Valeria and Roberto. Valeria looked at Pagani carefully. She noticed that he wore a lot of gold jewellery. There was a large and ugly gold ring on the little finger of his left hand. Pagani smiled at her.

'I am sorry to interrupt your meal,' he said. 'I came to see my friend Mario.'

'Don't worry,' said Roberto. 'Please sit down. We can have some coffee together.'

Mario told a waiter to bring four coffees. Then he turned to

Pagani and said, 'I was speaking to my nephew about his farm. I'd like to buy it, but he doesn't want to sell it to me.'

Pagani smiled. 'How big is your farm?' he asked Roberto.

'I've got about one hundred hectares,' Roberto said. 'It's not a big farm.'

'How much are you offering to pay him?' Pagani asked Mario.

'One thousand million lire,' replied Mario.

'Good heavens!' said Pagani to Roberto. 'If you put that money in the bank, the interest would be about eighty million lire every year. Not many people earn that much money a year. You wouldn't need to work any more. You'd be a very rich young man.'

'Perhaps I wouldn't need to work,' said Roberto, 'but I'm happy as I am. I like working.'

'He won't change his mind,' Mario said. 'He doesn't want to be rich. He's not like other young men.'

'You're right, Uncle,' said Roberto. 'I am different from other men. Most of them want to be rich. They'll do anything to be rich. And they think if they are rich they'll be happy. I earn enough money now, and I'm doing what I want to do. That's more important to me than being rich. I'm not going to sell you my farm, Uncle. You can't make me change my mind.'

The waiter arrived with the coffee. Everyone was silent as the waiter put the cups of coffee on the table. Pagani drank his coffee quickly.

'Well, Mario,' he said, 'I came here to speak to you about business.'

'Of course,' said Mario, finishing his coffee. 'Let's go into my office.'

Mario and Pagani stood up and Pagani said goodbye. Then they left Valeria and Roberto alone.

'I didn't like that man, Pagani, did you?' Valeria said.

'He was all right,' said Roberto.

'A man called Pagani is the town councillor who is in charge

'I am different from other men,' said Roberto. 'Most of
them want to be rich. They'll do anything to be rich.'

of the Town Planning Department. I think he's the man who stopped me getting the job as Assistant Architect.'

'How do you know this is the same Pagani?' asked Roberto. 'Pagani is a common surname. There are hundreds of Paganis in this town.'

'Well, I didn't like him,' said Valeria. 'Did you see all the gold jewellery he was wearing? And that horrible gold ring! I don't like men who wear jewellery like that.'

Roberto laughed. He kissed Valeria and held her hand. 'Let's not worry about Mr Pagani,' he said.

———

Mario and Pagani were drinking whisky in Mario's office. The door was closed because they did not want anyone to hear them.

'You can see the problem, can't you?' Mario was saying. 'You heard my nephew say he will never sell his farm. We'll have to forget our special business agreement. There's nothing we can do.'

Pagani drank some of his whisky. 'I'm not going to forget our special business agreement,' he said. 'And neither are you.'

'But what can we do?' asked Mario. 'He won't sell.'

'I'm sorry about that,' said Pagani slowly. 'It's very unfortunate for him.'

'For him?' said Mario. 'Don't you mean it's unfortunate for us?'

Pagani smiled. 'I told you in the beginning that our agreement could be dangerous. We'll have to be very careful from now on, otherwise we could be in a lot of trouble.'

'What are you saying?' asked Mario. 'I don't understand.' He was beginning to get worried.

'If your nephew won't sell his farm, we'll have to make him sell it. I have a plan. It's very simple.'

'A plan?' asked Mario.

'Yes,' said Pagani. 'Give me some more whisky. Then I'll tell you what you've got to do.'

10

Fire!

A week had passed since Pagani had explained his plan. Mario was worried and unhappy. He was tired too. He had not slept well since he had heard the plan.

The last customers left the restaurant at about half past midnight. Mario was all alone. One hour later he locked the front door of the restaurant and switched off the lights. Then he sat in his office in the dark and waited.

He waited and thought about what he was going to do. At two o'clock the church bell rang in the distance. It was time to go.

Mario opened the back door of the restaurant and went outside into the dark empty courtyard. There was a store-room at the end of the courtyard where Mario kept his bicycle. He walked across the courtyard and went into the store-room. There was a large plastic container near the door. It was full of petrol. Mario picked up the container and put it in the bicycle basket. Then he wheeled the bicycle out of the store-room and closed the door behind him. Five minutes later he was cycling along the quiet lanes outside the town.

Soon Mario came to a bridge over a canal. He stopped and got off his bicycle. Then he pushed the bicycle to the side of the bridge. He placed the bicycle against a wall and took the plastic container from the basket. He began walking along the footpath beside the canal. After he had walked about fifty metres he stopped and looked over the field to his right. There, in the distance, were the buildings of Roberto's farm – the farmhouse, the barn and the animal sheds. Everything was dark and silent.

Mario walked across the fields, past the sleeping cows, and hid behind the cowshed. Mario moved round to the side of the shed and looked up at the farmhouse. It was quiet and there were no lights anywhere.

Mario opened the plastic container and began pouring petrol on the outside of the chicken shed. He worked quickly and quietly. The smell of petrol filled the air. Then Mario poured petrol inside the cowshed. Next he moved to the barn. This was where Valeria kept her horse. Mario poured petrol over the wooden sides of the barn. The horse moved about inside, stamping its feet.

The farmhouse had a wooden porch[18] which was near the barn and the farmhouse. Grapevines grew over the porch. Mario had a little petrol left in his container. He looked at the porch and the grapevines for a few moments. Then he emptied the petrol container around the bottom of the porch and around the farmhouse door.

Mario's hands were shaking. He took some matches from his pocket. He lit some matches and threw them against the door of the barn. Then he ran to the cowshed and lit some more matches. He threw the rest of the matches onto the petrol outside the chicken shed. Then he ran back across the field towards the canal.

On the canal footpath Mario tripped and fell. He lay on the ground breathing heavily. His heart was beating fast and hard. The smell of the petrol made him feel sick.

Mario stood up slowly and looked behind him. Bright red flames lit the dark night. The farm buildings were burning.

Ten minutes later, Mario was back at the restaurant. As he was putting away his bicycle in the store-room, he heard the sound of fire engines.

———

Roberto was having a strange dream. In his dream, he was cooking something in the oven. The kitchen was hot. Too hot. The windows and doors were closed. Roberto tried to open them,

*Mario's hands were shaking ... He threw the rest of the
matches onto the petrol outside the chicken shed.*

but he could not do it. Smoke began to come from the oven. The food was burning. Smoke filled the small kitchen. Roberto could not get out.

Roberto woke up suddenly. The bedroom was filling with smoke! It was difficult to breathe. Roberto jumped out of bed and went to the door. But it was not possible to escape that way. Flames were coming up the stairs.

Roberto went to the window and opened the shutters. Outside he could see that the farm buildings were on fire. He turned towards the door again. Now there were flames coming under the door. Roberto could not escape down the stairs.

He turned back to the window, climbed onto the window ledge and jumped down.

From where he was lying, he could hear the horse screaming in fear. He slowly pulled himself up to his feet. He felt a terrible pain in his right leg. He hobbled[19] towards the burning barn, pulled open the heavy barn door and looked inside.

Through the flames and smoke, he could see the terrified horse. He grabbed a horse blanket[20] and threw it over the horse's head. He untied the horse and led it out to safety. That was the last thing he remembered.

11

Inspector Pavone Asks Some Questions

The next day everybody in the town was talking about the fire. Mario was pleased to hear that his nephew was in hospital. Mario had not wanted to kill Roberto. He had wanted to destroy the farm.

Early in the morning, Mario drove to the farm to see what had happened. Almost nothing was left of the farm. The chicken shed had disappeared completely. The walls of the cowshed were black and twisted. Only one wall of the barn was standing. The rest of the barn had fallen down. The tractors and other farm equipment were so badly burnt that they could never be used again. The farmhouse had no roof. The walls were black and the furniture inside it was completely destroyed. Smoke was rising from the ground.

A few firemen were walking about the farmyard. The Fire Chief was writing notes in a little book. Mario watched the firemen for a few minutes and then he walked back to his car. Pagani's plan was working. Now all Mario and Pagani had to do was wait.

———

Roberto had been lucky not to die. He had breathed in the thick smoke and his back was burned. And when he had jumped out of the window he had broken his right leg.

Valeria came to visit him in hospital. Roberto's first question was about Valeria's horse.

'He's alive, thanks to you,' said Valeria. 'He was burnt, but not too badly. He'll be all right.'

'What about the other animals?' asked Roberto.

'The cows were in the field and weren't burnt at all,' said Valeria. 'But I'm afraid all the chickens died.'

About a week after the fire a policeman came to see Roberto. His name was Inspector Pavone. He was a big tall man with dark curly hair.

The inspector introduced himself and sat down next to Valeria, beside Roberto's bed.

'I've come to speak to you about the fire,' the inspector said. 'The fireman have found out how the fire started. It wasn't an accident. Someone deliberately set fire to the buildings. They used petrol to make the fire burn more quickly.'

Roberto could not believe it. 'But who would want to burn my farm down?'

'That's what I want to find out,' said the inspector. 'Did you see or hear anything unusual that night?'

'No,' Roberto said. 'I was tired and went to bed early, about ten o'clock. I slept very deeply. I woke up suddenly and found the bedroom was full of smoke.'

'I see,' said Inspector Pavone. 'Can you tell me about the insurance[21]? The farm is insured, isn't it?'

'Yes,' said Roberto.

'How much money will the insurance company pay you?' asked the inspector.

'I can't remember,' Roberto said. 'But I know it's not enough money to build the farm again.'

'So you won't profit from the fire?' asked the inspector.

'Of course not,' said Roberto.

'Will anyone else profit now that the farm has burned down?' the inspector asked.

'No one,' said Roberto.

'Can you think of anyone who would like to hurt you, to kill you perhaps?'

'No one at all. I'm perfectly sure about that, Inspector.'

'You have no enemies then,' said the inspector.

'None.'

'So there's no reason at all for anyone to have started the fire?' the inspector asked.

'No reason at all,' said Roberto.

'Could a crazy person have done it?' asked Valeria.

'I've heard of people who set buildings on fire because they like to watch the buildings burn.'

'That's true,' said Inspector Pavone. 'Perhaps some crazy person burned the farm down. We're investigating.'

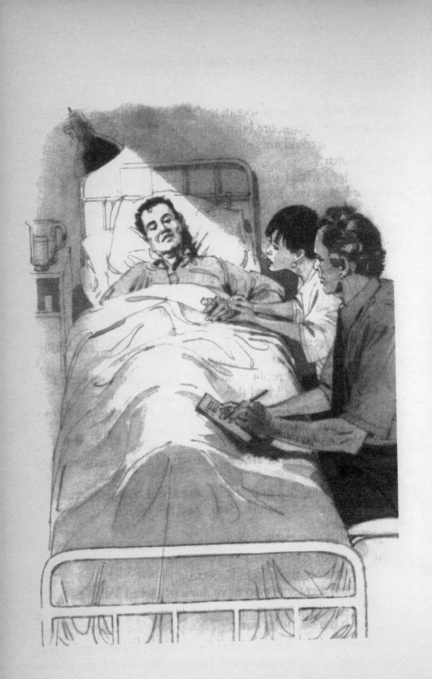

'Can you think of anyone who would like to hurt you, to kill you perhaps?' asked Inspector Pavone.

The inspector stood up. 'Thank you for answering my questions,' he said. 'If either of you can think of anything that may help my investigation, please telephone me.'

'We will,' said Roberto.

The inspector said goodbye and left the hospital.

12

Roberto Makes a Decision

Roberto got better slowly, but he felt very unhappy. He did not know what he was going to do.

'What am I going to do now?' he said to Valeria. 'How can I build the farm again?'

'I don't know, Roberto,' she said. 'We'll try to find a way.'

But the truth was that Roberto would not be able to rebuild the farm. It would cost too much money. The farm buildings and the farmhouse had been insured. But they had not been insured for enough. He would not even have enough money to rebuild the farmhouse. And worse still, it would be some months before Roberto could work again. He would not be able to earn any money for some time.

'I'll have to speak to Uncle Mario,' Roberto said quietly, to Valeria. 'But perhaps it's too late for that now.'

'Too late for what?' asked Valeria.

'Too late to sell him the farm. All I can do now is sell him the land. I have no buildings or farm equipment to sell.'

'Oh, Roberto, must you really sell everything?' said Valeria.

'What else can I do?' said Roberto. 'I don't want to sell it. I was born on that farm. Our family has always worked and lived there. And I promised my father before he died that I would not sell it. But I'm afraid there's nothing else I can do now. If I sell the farm to

41

my uncle, it will still belong to the Bonetti family. Will you go and speak to him? Tell him that I'll sell him the farm.'

'All right, Roberto,' said Valeria. 'If you're really sure there's nothing else you can do . . .'

'I'm sure,' said Roberto sadly.

———

Mario could not believe how lucky he was. Pagani's plan had worked! Now the special business agreement was going to be a success. And Mario was going to be very, very rich.

After Valeria had been to see him, Mario phoned Pagani and told him the good news. Then Mario went straight to the hospital to see Roberto.

Mario sat down beside the bed.

'I'm sorry about the farm,' Mario said.

Roberto looked at Mario and nodded his head, but he did not say anything.

'Valeria tells me you want to sell the farm now,' said Mario.

'Are you still interested?' asked Roberto.

'You know, Uncle, that I made a promise to my father,' Roberto said.

'Yes,' said Mario. 'You promised not to sell the farm. But if your father was alive now, he would understand.'

'My father wanted our family to go on working on the land. And that's what I want too.'

'I know,' said Mario.

'So I agree to sell you that farm because you're my uncle,' said Roberto, 'my father's brother.'

'You're doing the right thing,' said Mario. 'Don't worry, Roberto. I'll take care of everything.'

'Thank you, Uncle,' said Roberto. 'I know you will.'

When Mario went away, Roberto lay quietly in his bed. He felt very sad. Selling the farm was like selling a part of himself. Roberto's life would never be the same again.

13

A Newspaper Report

It was now almost the end of August. Roberto had left hospital. He had nowhere to live, so he was staying with Valeria, at her parent's house. Mario came several times to talk about the farm. The sale of the farm was arranged for Monday, 14th September. On that date, Mario and Roberto would sign the contract of sale[22].

On 2nd September, Mario heard some terrible news. Pagani had been arrested by the police. There was a report about the arrest in the local newspaper.

COUNCILLOR PAGANI ARRESTED *Police have arrested Town Councillor, Mr Luca Pagani. Mr Pagani, who is in charge of the Town Planning Department, had been receiving payments from a local businessman called Franco Goldoni. Mr Goldoni had been making payments to Mr Pagani so that the factory inspectors would not close his factory.*

Mr Goldoni owns a small chemical company and his factory produces dangerous chemicals. But Mr Goldoni's factory was not safe. When Councillor Pagani looked around the factory, he did not ask Mr Goldoni to make the factory safe. Instead, he asked Mr Goldoni for money. Goldoni paid the money. Pagani did nothing about closing the unsafe factory.

'I paid every month for three years,' said Mr Goldoni. 'Last month Mr Pagani asked me to give him more money. But I could not pay this money. So I decided to tell the police. I know there are other businessmen in this town who pay money to Mr Pagani. He is a criminal and he must be punished.'

Mr Pagani is under house arrest. He cannot leave his own home. He will have to appear in court on 11th September.

Mario put down the newspaper. This was terrible news. Pagani would probably go to prison. Mario did not know what to do. He was very worried. He was not worried about Pagani. He was worried about himself and about the special business agreement.

Mario needed Pagani to help him buy the farm. Mario did not have money. Pagani knew important people who worked in a bank. He was going to arrange a big loan of money. Mario could not do this on his own. He needed Pagani's help.

How can I buy the farm now? Mario thought. What will happen to the special business agreement?

Money was only one problem. There were others. Roberto's farm was agricultural land. It was not possible to build on it. Mario needed Pagani's help with the Town Planning Department. Pagani would be able to change the agricultural land to building land if he was in charge of the Town Planning Department. But now Pagani would probably go to prison. And he would never be a town councillor again.

There was one other problem. This problem was terrible to think about. Perhaps the police would find out about the special business agreement. If the police found out about it, then Mario would be in trouble as well. Mario had to speak to Pagani immediately.

Mario picked up the phone and rang Pagani's number.

'Hello,' said a voice.

'Hello, Mr Pagani,' Mario said, his voice shaking. 'It's me, Mario Bonetti.'

'You've heard about my arrest, have you?' said Pagani.

'Yes,' said Mario. 'I'm very sorry.'

'Don't worry,' Pagani said. 'I know a good solicitor[23]. I won't go to prison. I'll have to pay a fine[24], that's all.'

'And what about our special business agreement?' asked Mario.

'We go on as planned. We can't stop now.'

'Won't the police find out?' asked Mario.

44

'Hello, Mr Pagani,' Mario said, his voice shaking.
'It's me, Mario Bonetti.'

'Of course not,' said Pagani. 'I won't tell the police, and neither will you. Nobody else knows about it.'

'But there's another problem,' said Mario. 'You won't be in charge of the Planning Department any more.'

'And so?'

'Well, we can't build on the farmland, can we?' Mario went on. 'It's not building land.'

'Don't worry,' Pagani said. 'It *is* building land now. Everything will be all right, you'll see.'

'Good,' said Mario. 'Then there's no need to worry.'

'No need to worry at all.'

14

Valeria Starts Work

Two days after Pagani's arrest, on Friday, Valeria had a call from the Architects' Office. Mr Galli had some good news for her.

'Are you still interested in the job of Assistant Architect?' he asked.

'Oh, yes!' replied Valeria. She couldn't believe it was true.

'Good,' said Mr Galli. 'You can start on Monday morning. Be here at nine o'clock.'

On Monday morning, Mr Galli introduced Valeria to the other people working in the office. Then he spoke to Valeria in private.

'Were you surprised to get my telephone call?' he asked, as they sat down in his office.

'I was a little surprised at first,' Valeria said. 'But I read about Mr Pagani's arrest and then I remembered what you had told me.'

'Of course,' said Galli.

'So it's true,' said Valeria, 'that it was Pagani who stopped me getting the job?'

'Unfortunately,' said Galli, 'when you came to see me, I couldn't tell you everything. I wasn't completely sure of the truth myself. I asked if you knew Pagani because I wanted to find out *why* he didn't want you here.'

'And do you know the truth now?' asked Valeria.

'I'm afraid I don't,' said Galli. 'All I know for certain is that he didn't want you here.'

'How can you be certain?'

'Pagani told me that the Planning Department had spent too much money,' Galli began. 'He said I couldn't have a new Assistant Architect because every office in the department had to save money. But Pagani wasn't telling the truth. I spoke to people in other offices. Pagani had not asked them to save money. And Pagani hadn't saved money in other ways. It wasn't true that we had to save money. Pagani told me to do it because he didn't want our office to have a new Assistant Architect.'

'But why?' asked Valeria.

'I'm afraid I don't know,' said Galli. 'But Pagini isn't an honest man. We know that now. I'm sure he had a good reason.'

'I wish I knew what that reason was,' said Valeria. 'I can't understand why he wouldn't want me to work here.'

Valeria thought for a moment. 'This Mr Pagani . . . ,' she said, ' . . . is he a tall, dark-haired man who wears a lot of gold jewellery? Aged about forty-five?'

'That's him,' said Galli.

'Then I *have* met him,' said Valeria. 'He's a friend of my boyfriend's uncle – Mario Bonetti.'

'The restaurant owner?'

'Yes.'

'That's interesting,' said Galli. 'Perhaps Pagani knew about you from Mario Bonetti.'

'Perhaps,' said Valeria. 'But I still don't understand why he didn't want me to work here.'

'Well, we may never know the reason,' said Galli. 'Pagani is in trouble with the police. He'll probably go to prison and he won't ever come back to the Planning Department. You've got your job here now. Perhaps we should forget about it.'

'I'm sure you're right,' said Valeria.

'And now let me tell you about the job,' said Galli. 'You've got a lot to learn!'

15

New Land for Building

Everybody in the town thought that Pagani would go to prison. But they were wrong. The trial was on 11th September. The judge ordered Pagani to pay a big fine. He did not send him to prison.

Now there was nothing to stop Mario buying the farm from Roberto. Pagani went to see his friends at the bank. He arranged for Mario to get the money he needed.

Soon it was 14th September. On that day, Roberto would sell the farm to Mario. An appointment had been made at a solicitor's office in the town. The appointment was for half past three.

14th September was a hot, dry day. At breakfast, Roberto said to Valeria, 'This is the saddest day of my life. Selling the farm is worse than seeing it burn down.'

Valeria was busy at work in the Architects' Office. She did not have much time to think about the sale of the farm to Mario. Today they were making some drawings for a new sports centre.

In the early afternoon, Valeria was sent to get some documents[25] about the new sports centre. All the documents of the

Town Planning Department were kept in a large room. There were thousands of papers and drawings here. The room was full of big filing cabinets and cupboards.

Valeria was looking for the Council Report on the new sports centre. But it wasn't easy to find. Some of the papers were not in the right place. Valeria put a pile of papers onto a table and began to look through them carefully. It was then that she noticed a report at the bottom of the pile. She saw Pagani's name on the first page. She read the title: NEW LAND FOR BUILDING: A *Report by Councillor Luca Pagani*. This was interesting. Valeria saw the date: 15th August. So Pagani had written this report a few days before he was arrested.

Valeria began to read the report. The report said that new building land was needed because more people were living in the town. Some agricultural land would have to be used for building.

Valeria turned the pages and saw some maps. Parts of these maps were coloured pink. The pink areas showed where the new building land was going to be. On one of the maps Valeria saw Roberto's farm. The farm was right in the middle of a pink area. Valeria knew immediately that building land was worth ten times as much as agricultural land. Mario was going to pay Roberto one thousand million lire. But the land was now really worth ten thousand million lire. This was a fortune.

Valeria thought about everything that had happened recently. Pagani had stopped her getting the job in the Architects' Office. Mario had tried to buy the farm. Then someone had burned down the farm. This had forced Roberto to sell it. Mario and Pagani were friends, and Pagani had written this report about new building land. Mario had said that he wanted to keep horses on the farm. Valeria suddenly understood that this was not true.

Valeria was horrified. Now she understood. Mario and Pagani were working together. They had burnt down the farm. They had nearly killed Roberto.

Valeria looked at her watch. It was after half past two. At half

The pink areas showed where the new building land
was going to be.

past three Roberto and Mario would sign the contract of sale. There was no time to lose.

Valeria telephoned the police station immediately and asked to speak to Inspector Pavone.

'I'm phoning about the fire at the Bonetti farm,' Valeria said. 'Roberto told you that no one could profit if the farm burned down. But that's not true. I've found someone who will.'

'Who's that?' asked Inspector Pavone.

'Mario Bonetti. He'll profit from the fire. And I believe Luca Pagani will profit too. I think they're working together.'

'Why didn't you tell me this before?'

'Because I didn't know before,' said Valeria. 'I only found out about five minutes ago!'

Valeria told the inspector about Pagani's report. Then she told him how Pagani had stopped her getting the job in the Architects' Office.

'Pagani didn't want me in the Architects' Office because he knew I might find out about the new land for building.'

'This is very interesting,' said Inspector Pavone. 'Mario Bonetti will certainly profit from buying the land. But that's not enough to prove he burned down the farm. Unfortunately we have no proof that he and Pagani were working together.'

Valeria began to feel very unhappy. She looked at her watch again. It was now nearly three o'clock. In half an hour Roberto and Mario would sign the contract of sale. The farm would belong to Mario, and then Mario could do what he wanted with it. Neither she nor Roberto could stop him.

'The information you have given me is very important,' the inspector said. 'You've been very helpful. I'm sure we'll be able to find the proof that we need.'

'At half past three the farm will be sold,' said Valeria. 'Then we won't be able to do anything. And you may never find enough proof. I must stop Roberto signing the contract of sale before it's too late.'

'Where are they signing the contract?'

'At a solicitor's office in Via Roma.'

'I'll take you there in my car,' the inspector said. 'Wait for me outside the Town Hall. We'll be at the solicitor's office before half past three.'

16

The Solicitor's Office

Via Roma was one of the main shopping streets. There were shops on both sides of the street. Above the shops were flats and offices. The solicitor's office was on the first floor of a large building. There was an expensive clothes shop on the ground floor.

Inspector Pavone parked his car in front of the clothes shop.

'Thank you, Inspector,' said Valeria, and got out of the car.

The inspector got out too. 'I'm coming with you,' he said. 'I want to speak to your boyfriend's uncle.'

Valeria and Inspector Pavone entered the building and walked up the stairs to the first floor. The solicitor's office was at the end of the corridor. They hurried down the corridor and went inside. It was exactly thirty-two minutes past three.

'Can I help you?' a secretary said.

'Where's Mr Bonetti?' Valeria asked.

'Which Mr Bonetti?' asked the secretary.

'Both,' said Valeria sharply. 'It's very urgent.'

'They've just gone in to see the solicitor,' the secretary said. She pointed to a room on her right. 'Would you like to wait?'

Valeria did not answer. She went straight into the solicitor's private office.

'Hey! Wait a minute!' shouted the secretary.

But Valeria had already gone in. Inspector Pavone smiled at the secretary and followed Valeria.

The solicitor was sitting at his desk. Roberto and Mario were sitting opposite him. They all turned and stared as Valeria and the inspector walked in.

'Don't sign the contract, Roberto!' Valeria shouted. 'Your uncle is a liar and a cheat. He's not told us the truth.'

Mario went red in the face. He was very angry. 'What are you saying?' he shouted at Valeria. 'Have you gone crazy?'

'No, Mr Bonetti, I have not,' Valeria said firmly.

Valeria turned to Roberto. 'I'm sorry, Roberto,' she said. 'Your uncle hasn't told us the truth. He's not going to keep horses on the farm. He's going to use the land for building. Isn't that right, Mr Bonetti?'

'You're completely crazy,' said Mario. 'Roberto, don't listen to her.'

Now the solicitor became angry. 'What's happening here? And what are you doing here?' he said, looking at Valeria and the inspector.

'Let me explain,' said the policeman. 'My name's Pavone, Inspector Pavone.'

'A policeman!' said the solicitor.

'Yes, sir,' said the inspector. 'I'm afraid I must ask this gentleman to come with me to the police station.' The inspector pointed at Mario.

'We're doing important business here!' said Mario angrily. 'You'll have to wait.'

'No, that's not possible,' the inspector said. 'I think your business here has finished. I can't allow you to sign that contract of sale.'

'Why not?' asked Mario.

'I'll explain everything at the police station,' said the inspector calmly. 'Please come with me.'

Mario stood up slowly.

'Don't sign the contract, Roberto!' Valeria shouted.
'Your uncle is a cheat and a liar.'

'You needn't worry now, Miss Conti,' the inspector said to Valeria. 'I'll speak to you and Roberto again soon.' And he turned and led Mario out of the office.

17

A Plan for the Future

After Valeria and Roberto had left the solicitor's office, Valeria explained everything. She told Roberto about Pagani's report on the new building land.

'I suddenly understood,' she said, 'why Mario wanted to buy the farm. He and Pagani were working together, I'm sure. They must have burned the farm down, Roberto. They could have killed you!'

'I can't believe it,' Roberto said. 'My own uncle wouldn't do that. It's impossible.'

'But it must be true, Roberto,' Valeria said. 'It's the only explanation.'

It *was* the only explanation. But Roberto did not want to believe it.

In the evening, Roberto had to change his mind. Soon after dinner, Inspector Pavone telephoned and asked to speak to Roberto.

'Your uncle has told us everything,' the inspector said. 'He burned your farm down to make you sell it.'

The inspector then explained all about the special business agreement.

'Pagani knew that land prices would go up when a big computer company moved to the town,' he said. 'Pagani and your uncle wanted to build shops and houses on your land so that they could sell them for a profit. They would have made a fortune!'

Roberto could not speak. His own uncle had lied to him, and he had almost killed him.

'Your uncle and Pagani are both criminals,' the inspector said. 'Pagani nearly went to prison a short time ago. But he'll definitely go to prison now.'

'And my uncle?' asked Roberto.

'He'll go to prison too,' said the inspector. 'Your uncle is a foolish and greedy man. He got himself into some very dangerous business. He could have killed you.'

'I know that,' said Roberto sadly. 'I won't ever be able to forget it.'

———

The inspector was right. Mario and Pagani both went to prison. Roberto did not feel happy or sad about that. He did not feel angry either. He was too shocked to feel anything.

Some months passed. Roberto began to think about the future.

One cold Saturday morning, Roberto and Valeria walked over the fields which Roberto had once farmed. Everywhere was covered in snow. Nobody had done anything to the farm since the fire. Roberto and Valeria looked around. It was a very sad sight.

Roberto held Valeria close to him. 'I've been thinking about the future,' he said. 'I've decided what I want to do.'

Valeria looked at Roberto and kissed him. 'That's good,' she said.

'You know, my uncle had a very good idea,' Roberto said. He pointed at all the land around them.

'What?' said Valeria, surprised. 'I can't believe it! You aren't going to build houses and shops here, are you?'

Roberto laughed. 'No, I'm not,' he said. 'My uncle said he was going to keep horses. I think that's a good idea. I'll have a new house built and stables. It'll be something small to start with.

People will keep their horses here. Others will come to learn how to ride. What do you say?'

Valeria smiled. 'It's a lovely idea, Roberto. But it'll cost a lot of money. Where will you get the money from?'

'I've worked it all out,' Roberto said. 'I'll sell a few hectares of the land. That will give me the money to rebuild the farmhouse and build some stables. I'll have some land for the horses and I'll keep some fields for grass. The grass will be useful for the horses. It'll be much better than keeping cows and chickens.'

'And it'll make a nice home too,' said Valeria.

'Yes, it will,' Roberto said. 'It'll be a beautiful home for you and me.'

Points for Understanding

1

1 Describe the little square where Mario Bonetti was sitting.
2 Who came to see Mario Bonetti?
3 What promise did Mario make?

2

1 What was going to happen to make the price of land go up?
2 What was the special agreement?
3 What advantage would Pagani and Mario have?
4 What are the differences between farmland and building land?
5 How would Pagani be able to change the law?

3

1 Why was life difficult for Roberto?
2 What did Roberto promise his dying father?

4

1 Who was Valeria Conti?
2 'Please let me know if you need help,' said Mario to Roberto.
   (a) Why would Roberto need help on the farm?
   (b) What was Mario's real reason for offering to help Roberto?

5

1 Describe Roberto's farm.
2 What was Valeria studying?
3 What were Roberto and Vateria's reasons for celebration?
4 'Why do you want to buy the farm?' Valeria asked Mario. What was Mario's reply?

6

1 'There are a few problems,' Mario said to Pagani.
   What were the problems?

2 How was Pagani going to solve the problem with Valeria?
3 How was Pagani going to try to solve the problem with Roberto?

7

1 What did Pagani order Giorgio Galli to do?
2 Why did Galli decide to speak to other people in the Planning Department?
3   (a) Describe Pagani's visit to the dirty old factory.
       (b) Why do you think Goldoni hated Pagani?

8

1 Why was Valeria crying?
2 Describe Valeria's meeting with Galli.

9

1 What did Valeria notice about Pagani?
2 What did Pagani say to Roberto?
3 How was Roberto different from other men?
4 What was Pagani planning to do if Roberto would not sell the farm?

10

1 Describe how Mario set fire to the farm.
2 How did Roberto escape from the burning farmhouse?
3 Describe how Roberto saved Valeria's horse.

11

1 How much of the farm was destroyed in the fire?
2 Why did Inspector Pavone want to know who would profit from the fire?

12

1 Why was Roberto going to have to sell the farm?
2 Why did Roberto think Mario was the right person to buy the farm?

13

1 Why was Pagani arrested?
2 What three problems did Mario have after Pagani's arrest?
3 What were Pagani's answers to these problems?

14

1 How was Mr Galli sure that it was Pagani who stopped Valeria from getting the job in the Architects' Office?
2 Did Galli know why Pagani had stopped Valeria from getting the job?

15

1 How did the judge punish Pagani?
2 What was the date and time of the sale of Roberto's farm?
3 How did Valeria find out the real value of Roberto's farm?
4 What did Valeria tell Inspector Pavone on the phone?
5 Why did Valeria and the inspector have to hurry to get to the solicitor's office?

16

1 Mario went red in the face. He was very angry. Why was Mario so angry?
2 Who stopped the sale of the land?

17

1 The inspector explained to Roberto all about the special business agreement. Explain the agreement in detail.
2 What did Inspector Pavone say would happen to Luca Pagani and Mario Bonetti?
3 'I've been thinking about the future,' said Roberto. What were Roberto's plans for the future?

Glossary

1 **forties** – *a man in his forties* (page 4)
a man who is between forty and fifty years old. This is a way of speaking about someone when you do not know their exact age.

2 **know** – *a useful man to know* (page 4)
an important man. If you make friends with him, he can help you in your business.

3 **deserted** (page 6)
a piece of ground that is not being used and has no one taking care of it is called deserted.

4 **block** – *office block* (page 6)
a tall building with many offices inside it.

5 **centre** – *research centre* (page 6)
a building in which scientific investigations are carried out.

6 **advantage** – *to have an advantage* (page 8)
to know more than someone else so that you are in a better position to know what to do.

7 **Town Planning Department** (page 9)
new houses, schools, roads etc. have to be planned in every town or city. The planning is done by architects and engineers. The architects draw the buildings and suggest where they should be built. The town council makes the decisions about where the buildings should go.

8 **firmly** (page 18)
to speak in a way which shows that no one can easily make you change your mind.

9 **restore** (page 18)
to build something up again and make it look new.

10 **broken** – *a promise can be broken* (page 20)
this shows the kind of man Pagani is. He does not believe that a person has to keep promises.

11 **developments** – *building developments* (page 21)
if Valeria Conti gets a job in the Architects' Office, she will know about plans for building new shops, offices, houses, factories etc in and around the town. So Valeria might find out about Pagani's plans to change Roberto's land from agricultural to building land.

12 **expecting** (page 23)
when you know someone is expecting you, you know the meeting has been arranged. The person is waiting for you.

13 *safe* (page 24)
a strong box, usually made of metal, in which money and valuables are kept.

14 *deliberately* (page 27)
if you do something deliberately, you do it for a clear reason. In this case, Galli does not know the reason.

15 *imagine* (page 29)
to have an idea about something which may be true or not true.

16 *confused* (page 29)
not able to think clearly.

17 *dessert* (page 30)
sweet food eaten at the end of a meal – eg ice cream.

18 *porch* (page 35)
a covering which goes over an entrance to a house.

19 *hobble* (page 37)
to walk with great difficulty because you cannot move your legs easily.

20 *blanket* – *horse blanket* (page 37)
a large piece of wool cloth used to cover horses.

21 *insurance* (page 39)
when anyone owns property, like the farm, they pay an amount of money every year to an insurance company. Then, if your property is damaged or something is stolen the insurance company will pay you the value of it. Some people try to cheat by insuring their property for more than it is worth. That is why Inspector Pavone asks Roberto how much the farm is insured for.

22 *sale* – *contract of sale* (page 43)
a written agreement which has to be signed by the person who is buying and the person who is selling some property. When you have signed a contract the sale must happen. It is a legal agreement (legal means to do with the law).

23 *solicitor* (page 44)
a person who deals with business to do with the law, like the buying and selling of houses and land.

24 *fine* – *pay a fine* (page 44)
be ordered in a court by a judge to pay money to the court because you have done something wrong.

25 *documents* (page 48)
important papers on which there are plans or writing.

Shane *by Jack Schaefer*
Old Mali and the Boy *by D. R. Sherman*
Bristol Murder *by Philip Prowse*
Tales of Goha *by Leslie Caplan*
The Smuggler *by Piers Plowright*
The Pearl *by John Steinbeck*
Things Fall Apart *by Chinua Achebe*
The Woman Who Disappeared *by Philip Prowse*
The Moon is Down *by John Steinbeck*
A Town Like Alice *by Nevil Shute*
The Queen of Death *by John Milne*
Walkabout *by James Vance Marshall*
Meet Me in Istanbul *by Richard Chisholm*
The Great Gatsby *by F. Scott Fitzgerald*
The Space Invaders *by Geoffrey Matthews*
My Cousin Rachel *by Daphne du Maurier*
I'm the King of the Castle *by Susan Hill*
Dracula *by Bram Stoker*
The Sign of Four *by Sir Arthur Conan Doyle*
The Speckled Band and Other Stories *by Sir Arthur Conan Doyle*
The Eye of the Tiger *by Wilbur Smith*
The Queen of Spades and Other Stories *by Aleksandr Pushkin*
The Diamond Hunters *by Wilbur Smith*
When Rain Clouds Gather *by Bessie Head*
Banker *by Dick Francis*
No Longer at Ease *by Chinua Achebe*
The Franchise Affair *by Josephine Tey*
The Case of the Lonely Lady *by John Milne*

For further information on the full selection of
Readers at all five levels in the series, please refer
to the Heinemann Readers catalogue.

Macmillan Heinemann English Language Teaching, Oxford

A division of macmillan Publishers Limited

Companies and representatives throughout the world

ISBN 0 435 27249 7

Heinemann is a registered trade mark of Reed Educational and Professional Publishing Ltd

© Richard Prescott, 1993
First Published 1993

Illustrated by David Barnett
Typography by Adrian Hodgkins
Cover by Chris Brown and Threefold Design
Typeset in 11/12.5 pt Goudy
by Joshua Associates Ltd, Oxford
Printed and bound in Great Britain by Cox and Wyman

98 99 00 01 02 03 04 05 06